The Way of the Master

Seek and save the lost
the way Jesus did

Kirk Cameron   Ray Comfort

The Way of the Master
Intermediate Training Course Study Guide

Published by
The Way of the Master
A Ministry of Living Waters Publications
P.O. 1172
Bellflower, CA 90706

ISBN 1-878859-73-0

Edited by Lynn Copeland

Design and production by Genesis Group

Cover photographs by Carol J. Scott, CJ Studio, Covina, CA (www.cj-studio.com)

Cartoons by Richard Gunther

Printed in the United States of America

Unless otherwise indicated, Scripture quotations are from the *New King James* version, © 1979, 1980, 1982 by Thomas Nelson Inc., Publishers, Nashville, Tennessee.

Scripture references marked KJV are from the *King James Version*.

Contents

Getting Started

Welcome to The Way of the Master Intermediate Training Course. We trust that you've completed the Basic Training Course, and that you've gotten your evangelistic feet wet. By now you should have been gently coaxed out of your comfort zone and be sharing your faith biblically with your family, friends, and even strangers. You now have tools that help you deal with your fears, and you're learning to make evangelism a way of life. When you go to the grocery store, you go not just to buy food, but to pass out a tract because you know what matters most in this life. Someone's eternity is more important than what you're going to have for dinner tonight. You know that receiving a phone call from someone who dialed a wrong number is not a mistake—it's a divine opportunity for you to witness over the phone. Perhaps you even have a local "fishing hole" that you visit regularly to fish for men.

If these things are true for you, then the content of the Intermediate Training Course will serve to further fuel your evangelistic fire. As you've been out sharing your faith, you've likely encountered questions you're not sure how to answer. This course will give you additional training to help you know what to say so you can reach more people with the gospel.

Or perhaps you've understood the biblical principles taught in the Basic Training Course, but you're finding it difficult to put them into practice on a regular basis. If so, this course will help you gain more confidence to begin sharing your faith with others, even making it a regular part of your lifestyle. You, too, can discover the exhilaration that comes from sharing the gospel!

In the Intermediate Training Course you are going to learn about the critical subjects of true and false conversion, how to answer an evolutionist, how to witness to a family member, what to do "when things go wrong," how to speak to a homosexual, and other relevant topics that will further equip you to reach the lost.

HOW TO USE THIS COURSE

Although this course can be used for individual study, it is ideally suited for use in small and large groups. Evangelism can seem fearful and intimidating, and a group setting will provide the needed encouragement and accountability.

For group use, notes for the leader are highlighted in the lessons, and additional Leader's Helps are available on page 87. Be sure to review these in planning the study and preordering materials.

Included in the course are audio CDs containing the audio portion of the videos. These are useful for the leader to gain further preparation, for participants who miss viewing the video in the group session, or for anyone who wants to hear it again as a refresher.

Each lesson includes a video segment, discussion questions to help apply the teaching, homework assignments, and at-home Bible study. The video sessions are about 30 minutes in length. To allow adequate time for all the suggested activities, the recommended time for each weekly session is approximately an hour and a half.

Each lesson includes the following parts:

- **Open in Prayer:** Begin each lesson in prayer, asking God to give you a deeper understanding of His Word, particularly in the area of evangelism, and to give you greater boldness and a love for the lost.

- **Share Your Experiences:** As you put these principles into practice each week, hearing one another's experiences will deepen your commitment, as you discover the joy of being used by God to reach the lost effectively. Be sure to allow adequate time for this important interaction.

- **Point to Ponder:** Quietly read this thought-provoking text before viewing the video, to prepare your heart for the class.

- **View the Video:** Watch the video as a group.

- **Apply the Principles:** This section contains discussion questions to help you apply the principles taught in the video to your life. Depending on your group size, you may want to divide into smaller groups to discuss the questions. Allow each participant to express his thoughts, being careful to avoid arguing or having anyone dominate the conversation. Focus on the questions presented, and keep the session moving forward so you can get through the material in the available time. With a limited class time, select the questions you feel are most important for your group to discuss.

- **Quality Quote:** These pearls of wisdom, gleaned from evangelistic giants such as Charles Spurgeon, will help you focus on our sober responsibility to reach the lost. Bring each quote to life by having someone stand and proclaim it to the group. Don't just "read" it, but strive to reenact history by "preaching" it as though you were speaking to a congregation as the author himself!

- **Preacher's Progress:** "Eavesdrop" on these helpful witnessing conversations, written in the style of *Pilgrim's Progress* by John Bunyan. To make these more meaningful, perform them as a skit, with two confident volunteers playing the part of "Christian" and the other character ("Eva Lution," etc.). Assign these roles beforehand so the individuals can review the material and really put themselves into the role.

  "Set the stage" by arranging a couple of chairs (or other props), announce the characters' names, and describe the setting for that scene. Have fun with this as you act it out for the group.

- **Close in Prayer:** This will end the group time for this lesson. Be sure to pray for each other throughout the course, that no distractions would keep anyone from completing it. (It *will* be a battle!) You may want to make Ephesians 6:19,20 your daily prayer.

- **Break Out of Your Comfort Zone:** These weekly assignments are the most important part of the course. We are to be *doers* of the Word, not hearers only. Each week you will be challenged to stretch your evangelistic muscles, interact with others, and share what you have learned with the lost in your community.

  Each lesson will present you with two options: an Individual Activity and a Group Activity. *We strongly encourage everyone to read both options.* The Great Commission wasn't given as a once-a-week event, but as something we all should do *as we go*. Therefore, we are including ideas for how individuals can share their faith throughout their week, as well as ideas for group activities to perhaps inspire the entire church to get involved in outreach. Going as a group often increases participation, and provides mutual encouragement and accountability. You may want to do one activity, or both. Whichever you choose, commit to doing something each week so evangelism becomes a way of life for you. Keep the other ideas in mind for future reference.

You will be expected to share your experiences with others during the next session.

- **For Deeper Study:** While completing this Bible study portion of the homework is not essential to enjoy this course, we highly recommend that you do as much as possible. God's Word is powerful, and in searching it you will discover wonderful truths that reinforce what you're learning in class.

- **Memory Verse:** At the end of each homework assignment is a memory verse. Rather than the typical memory verses, which are designed to comfort the Christian, these are for use in witnessing to bring biblical truths to the lost.

- **Words of Encouragement:** These letters from others who are following "the way of the Master" will encourage you to persevere as you discover the joy of sharing the gospel daily. They may also give you ideas on how to implement the principles you are learning through this study.

REACHING THE GOAL

The goal of this course is not simply to have people complete its eight lessons, but to transform the lives of each of the participants. Therefore, we encourage you to put in whatever time and effort is needed to ensure that these principles sink in and are then lived out. The souls of the lost are far too valuable to do otherwise.

To help accomplish this goal, we encourage everyone participating in the course to listen to The Way of the Master Radio. We cannot tell you how excited we are to have this radio program as part of our ministry. For two hours each weekday, Christians can listen to a program that does nothing but equip them to reach out to the lost. There is nothing like this on the air. Where else can you hear witnessing to atheists, psychics, evolutionists, businessmen, housewives, university students, etc.—all happening live as you listen? Not only are Christians all around the world learning to share their faith as a lost person is being witnessed to, but any unsaved people who tune in are also hearing the biblical gospel!

With encouragement and accountability from the group, trusting in the Lord to help you, you can reach the goal of becoming bold, confident witnesses for Jesus Christ. May God richly bless you as you continue your journey of *biblical* evangelism, faithfully following the way of the Master.

RAY COMFORT
KIRK CAMERON

LESSON 1
Understanding True & False Conversions

▶ *Materials Needed: The Sample Pack of tracts included in the course; additional tracts if needed by participants*
Leader's Note: Begin the class by briefly sharing a little about yourself and why you are leading this course.

OPEN IN PRAYER

SHARE YOUR EXPERIENCES

As time allows, go around the room and, one at a time, stand and briefly state why you have come to this class. Share how you've progressed since beginning the Basic Training Course, and what you are hoping to accomplish by taking this course.

▶ *Leader's Note: Ask how many participants recall the two acronyms taught in the Basic Training Course: WDJD and CRAFT. As a refresher, take a moment to review them quickly. If participants no longer carry their Quick Reference Cards, you can find that information listed in Appendix A.*

POINT TO PONDER

I (Ray) was stuck in a flower shop one day. It was my wife's birthday, and I had asked an employee to put together a dozen roses for her. It was taking so long to arrange them,

I started to wonder if the person was growing them from seeds. I was so bored that I began sniffing all their plants. Immediately attracted to three beautiful orchids, I leaned over and sniffed. There was no smell. Perhaps they were the "smell-less" variety. I then decided to touch them, and realized that they were manmade. They were stiff and had dust on them. They were fakes!

I said to the employee, "You can tell the difference between what man makes and what God makes. God's flowers almost always have a fragrance." Then I began thinking about the differences. God's plants not only have an aroma, but they have growth. They have growth because they have life. Man's efforts have no smell and no growth, because they are not alive. They are inanimate. Dead.

There is a similar distinction between man's efforts and God's efforts to reach the lost. Man's "converts" have no aroma. False converts don't have a prayer life that ascends to the throne of God as a sweet-smelling incense. Neither do they have genuine growth. They make a profession of faith but fail to grow in the knowledge of God. They don't grow because they don't feed on the Word. They have no appetite to do so because the life of God isn't in them. They are not born again, but are dead in their trespasses and sins.

What a tragedy! There are millions who sit among God's people as if they were the planting of the Lord, but God knows the difference. May He help us to awaken these masses to their deception and their terrible plight.

VIEW THE VIDEO **Understanding True & False Conversions (33 minutes)**

Apply the Principles

1. Do you know someone who is "backslidden"? If so, why do you think that person fell away?

2. Had you ever been taught about the biblical reality of false conversions? Why do you think most Christians want to avoid talking about the topic of false conversion?

3. Kirk mentioned a former youth pastor who said he's no longer a Christian because "if God truly lived in the hearts of Christians there would be a big change." When people see hypocrisy, why do you think they choose to conclude that there's no God, rather than conclude that these may not be true Christians?

4. What parables relate to true and false conversions?

5. Do you think Judas was genuinely saved or a false convert? Why?

6. What damage can be done by a Christian who doesn't understand that there's such a thing as false conversion?

7. On the video, a girl said, "The greatest cause of atheism today is Christians who acknowledge Jesus with their lips but then deny Him by their lifestyles." What kind of harm is done by those who are false converts? How could you respond to her comment?

8. What would you say to someone you suspect is a false convert?

▶ *Leader's Note: Explain that this course contains a Sample Pack of tracts, which includes one each of 65–70 tracts. With such a great variety of tracts to choose from, participants are likely to find several to suit their personal tastes (from humorous to intellectual) and appeal to their intended audience. Give participants time to browse through the tracts to select their favorites, then place one order for the group, for the tracts they will be using throughout the course.*

QUALITY QUOTE

▶ *Leader's Note: Make sure you read this powerful quote with passion and conviction!*

> The false notion that they may be children of God while in a state of disobedience to his holy commandments; and disciples of Jesus though they revolt from his cross; and members of his true church, which is without spot or wrinkle, notwithstanding their lives are full of spots and wrinkles; is of all other deceptions upon themselves the most pernicious to their eternal condition. For they are at peace in sin and under a security in their transgression.
> —*William Penn*

PREACHER'S PROGRESS

The characters: Christian and Faye Kinnitt
Scene setting: Friday night outside a coffee house. It's packed. Christian is witnessing to a girl named Faye.

Faye Kinnitt: "Hey, I'm a Christian too."

Christian: "Really?"

Faye Kinnitt: "Yep. I invited Jesus into my heart a few years ago."

Christian: "Why are your friends laughing?"

Faye Kinnitt: "I dunno. I carry a Bible with me all the time. Here it is in my bag. I've had it for years."

Christian: "It looks new. Do you read it much?"

Faye Kinnitt: "Once or twice. My boyfriend and I have read it first thing in the morning."

Christian: "Do you live together?"

Faye Kinnitt: "Yes. But we don't do anything."

Christian: "Your friends are laughing again."

Faye Kinnitt: "I don't care what they think. Sex is okay if you love someone, and I love my boyfriend."

Christian: "So you were lying to me when you said that you don't do anything."

Faye Kinnitt: "Just a small lie."

Christian: "Do you think you will go to heaven when you die?"

Faye Kinnitt: "Yes."

Christian: "Why?"

Faye Kinnitt: "Because I'm a good person."

Christian: "According to God's standard, you're not. You've admitted that you are a liar and a fornicator, and the Bible says that liars and fornicators will not enter the kingdom of God. It says, 'All liars will have their part in the lake of fire.'"

Faye Kinnitt: "You're trying to scare me."

Christian: "I'm only telling you the truth because I care about you. I don't want you to go to hell; neither does God. Why would I say these things if they weren't true?"

Faye Kinnitt: "I guess you wouldn't . . ."

Christian: "Do you know that you're a hypocrite? That's why your friends laugh at you when you say you are a Christian. If you can't fool them, you surely can't fool God. I think you need to truly repent—that means to turn from all sin: sex before marriage, lying, hypocrisy. What do you think?"

Faye Kinnitt: "I think you're right."

▶ *Leader's Note: Review the "Break Out of Your Comfort Zone" assignments with participants, challenging them to invest the time to complete the activities. Provide participants with a small quantity of tracts if they need them for the homework.*

Break Out of Your Comfort Zone

This portion of the homework is not optional. To receive the maximum benefit from this course, you *must* commit to completing the "Break Out of Your Comfort Zone" activities. Whether you choose the individual or group activity—or both—it's very important to get out of your comfort zone and do something to reach the lost. You will also be expected to share your experiences during the next session.

1. *Individual Activity:* Do you like challenges? Here are two. First, pray this prayer every morning until the next lesson: "God, bring someone to me today who needs to hear the gospel." Pray it. Go on, we dare you. You may think this is just a meaningless exercise, but if you mean it, and if God is faithful (and we know He is), then get ready for Him to send lost people your way. If you cringe at the thought, remember that this is the very reason you exist. Be willing to give God just a few minutes out of each twenty-four hours that He gives you to speak to someone about Christ. Keep in mind that it is not only an honor to be used by God, but when you lay your head on your pillow at night, you will be so thankful you prayed the prayer and that God used you to point a sinner to the Savior.

   Second, determine to always carry gospel tracts with you. You'll be less likely to pass up witnessing opportunities if you use tracts, because they make the transition to spiritual things so much easier. One way to be sure you always have tracts is to *put your money where your mouth is.* Call a few friends who are like-minded and tell them that if they ever find you in public without gospel tracts, you will give them $20 (and then challenge them to do the same). More important than simply carrying tracts is giving them away. Make a commitment that every time you leave the house you will not return until you've given out at least one tract.

2. *Group Activity:* Pray daily for opportunities to witness; otherwise you may go for days (even weeks) when you don't speak to anyone about their salvation. See complacency as a pit of quicksand that you should avoid, because once you're in it, it's very difficult to get out. So continually remind yourself of the fate of the lost, and make plans to go out as a group to fish for men.

Take a small quantity of tracts to a mall and determine to give them all out. Prepare yourself so you won't be disappointed at the occasional rejection. After a predetermined time, meet together to talk about the experience. What were your emotions from the time you decided to break out of your comfort zone until you accomplished your goal? If you were fearful, when was your fear the highest? When did it leave? How did you feel when people responded warmly? If you were rejected, how did you deal with it? Was it a positive or negative experience? When will you do it again? If you don't determine in your heart to go out again, you probably won't. Then paraphrase your thoughts—and your commitment to continue being a faithful witness—into a verbal prayer.

For Deeper Study

While completing this section of the homework is not essential to enjoy this course, we highly recommend that you do as much as possible. God's Word is powerful and in searching it you will discover wonderful truths that reinforce what you're learning in class.

1. One of the most frightening portions of Scripture is Matthew 7:21–27, which tells us that many who consider themselves Christians will expect to enter heaven, and yet be cast into hell. Forever. Read these verses and list the evidences of those who are saved.

Words of Encouragement

I'm one of many in the church today that "gave his heart" to Jesus at a young age. I went to church, even went on missionary trips, but if anything I was on the chilly side of being lukewarm. I never gave a second thought to sharing my faith. Then, about a year and a half ago, when I saw your Way of the Master series, my life was turned upside down. I wept over my condition for days. I didn't know that God saw me as a lying thief, and a blasphemous adulterer. *I thought God smiled upon me. After all, I "gave my heart" to Him a long while ago and went to church.* I had no idea than sin was so *exceedingly* sinful. I was a false convert in every sense. As I wept over my condition it really started to sink in what He did to save me, and what He saved me from. If justice had its way, I'd be hellbound and well deserving of it...but thanks be to Him, I'm headed for an undeserved heaven!

How could I have trampled underfoot the blood of our Savior for so long? The Way of the Master course changed all that. I began to thirst for the Bible, and compassion for the lost swallowed me whole. I couldn't wait to share my faith. I have worn my family and friends out with what God has opened up to me!

I'm a corporate jet pilot and using my job, I'm able to witness and give out your tracts from Belize to N.Y., and everywhere in-between. Ray relates many things to airplanes and flying and this makes it easy for me to use them too, especially with other pilots. For the most part, pilots are a liberal bunch who scoff when witnessed to. Oh, but the look on their face when showing them their true state by using God's moral standard. It's amazing to see those strongholds pulled down so effectively. What a sharp sword it is and to think that it's used so little today.

I can't put this fire out! And I don't want to!

—Kevin C., Kentucky

Then list the things that were done by those who *thought* they were saved. Why were they condemned (verse 23)?

2. Matthew 13:23 tells us that only the good-soil hearer "hears the word and *understands* it." What is it that keeps sinners from understanding the gospel (see 2 Corinthians 4:4)?

If some people respond to the gospel without understanding, how would using the Law help to give them the understanding they lack? (See Romans 3:20; 7:13; Galatians 3:24.)

3. Read Acts 8:9–24. What makes it appear that Simon the sorcerer was converted?

What do these verses tell us about his true condition?

4. Based on this, can people "believe" and yet not be saved? If so, what necessary step have they omitted? (See James 2:19; Luke 3:13.)

5. P. Nasty, whom Ray witnessed to on the video, said that he "accepted the fact that Jesus Christ died for his sins." Read Acts 26:20. Is "accepting Jesus" sufficient for true conversion? Why or why not?

6. The book of 1 John gives us some "tests" to know if we have eternal life (1 John 5:13). What are some marks of a genuine follower of Christ?

1 John 2:5,6

1 John 2:29

1 John 3:22,23

1 John 4:20,21

MEMORY VERSE

"Now by this we know that we know Him, if we keep His commandments. He who says, 'I know Him,' and does not keep His commandments, is a liar, and the truth is not in him."

1 JOHN 2:3,4

LESSON 2
Taking the Greatest Gamble

OPEN IN PRAYER

SHARE YOUR EXPERIENCES

Did you pray for witnessing opportunities during the last week? What happened? In light of what you learned in the previous lesson about true and false conversions, can you think of people you should witness to whom you wouldn't have thought of previously? If so, how are you going to handle it?

POINT TO PONDER

Of the two Wesley brothers, John is most often quoted. But his famous brother, Charles, was not only a great hymn writer, he also had a deep concern for the lost. He wrote, "In the coach to London, I preached faith in Christ. A lady was extremely offended... and threatened to beat me. I declared I deserved nothing but hell; so did she, and must confess it before she could have a title to heaven. This was most intolerable to her."

His brother John was right when he said, "A Christian is the only sane person in a worldwide insane asylum." This blind world is insane to believe that there will be no Day of Justice, and that death is something that happens only to others. They are insane to neglect God's offer of eternal life.

It's only when we receive the Spirit of "power and love" that we also receive "a sound mind," and we must use that sound mind to do what we know we should.

This life is like a burning desert. Time is like water cupped in our hands. An ignorant man will let its precious drops fall through his fingers, not realizing that it is his very life. We must treat every valuable minute as though it were our last drop of time, because one day it will be. Remind yourself of that fact at the beginning of every day. A great preacher said that men have been taught to live by remembering that they must die. So use your time very wisely, and the wisest thing you can do with that most precious of commodities is to seek and save that which is lost.

VIEW THE VIDEO Taking the Greatest Gamble
(30 minutes)

Apply the Principles

1. Why do you think people like to gamble?
2. What is the greatest gamble in life? Why?
3. Explain the two strong evidences for the reality of hell.
4. Why do you think mankind goes to great lengths to bring criminals to justice?
5. How would you describe the concept of "circumstantial priorities" to a lost person?
6. What example could you give to those who believe the conscience is learned rather than something we're born with?
7. How would you answer those who say they don't have a conscience?
8. Why do people respond differently to the thought of Judgment Day?
9. Finish this verse: "What shall it profit a man ..."

10. How could you convince sinners not to gamble with their soul?

QUALITY QUOTE

▶ *Leader's Note: Preach this with passion and urgency. The harvest is great and the laborers are few.*

"Not called!" did you say? "Not *heard* the call," I think you should say. Put your ear down to the Bible, and hear him bid you go and pull sinners out of the fire of sin. Put your ear down to the burdened, agonized heart of humanity, and listen to its pitiful wail for help. Go stand by the gates of hell, and hear the damned entreat you to go to their father's house and bid their brothers and sisters, and servants and masters not to come there. And then look Christ in the face, whose mercy you have professed to obey, and tell him whether you will join heart and soul and body and circumstances in the march to publish his mercy to the world.
—*William Booth (founder of the Salvation Army)*

PREACHER'S PROGRESS

The characters: Christian and Sal Frighteous
Scene setting: Christian goes to his regular "fishing hole" at the mall to witness and runs into Sal, and follows up on their earlier conversation.

Christian: "Hi, Sally. Good to see you. Have you thought much about what we spoke of last time—that the Day is coming when God will judge the world according to His perfect standards?"

Sal Frighteous: "Yes, I have ... and it doesn't concern me because my god would never send anyone to hell."

Christian: "Do you realize that you are breaking the Second of the Ten Commandments by saying that?"

Sal Frighteous: "What do you mean?"

Christian: "You have made a god to suit yourself. Your god would never send anyone to hell, because he couldn't —he doesn't exist. He's a figment of your imagination. You have made a god you feel comfortable with. That's called idolatry, and it's the oldest sin in the Book. I did the same for many years before I became a Christian."

Sal Frighteous: "Well, I still believe that I am a good person. I believe in God and I go to church. I think God will let me into heaven because I am a good person."

Christian: "Sal, you believe that because the god you have created in your mind has a low standard of morality. Did you know that the God of the Bible—the God you will have to face on the Day of Judgment—commands you to be perfect in thought, word, and deed? He is perfect, and He will judge you with a perfect Law. That leaves you in big trouble without the Savior."

Don't hesitate to stress the reality of an actual day when God will bring her to give an account of her life. This is often the very thing that will awaken a self-righteous sinner, help her think seriously about her fate, and trust in the Savior.

CLOSE IN PRAYER

Break Out of Your Comfort Zone

1. *Individual Activity:* Go to www.WayoftheMasterRadio.com and listen to at least two programs. Catch the daily broadcast live, or browse through the archived shows to find topics that pique your interest. Listening in on live witnessing will help equip and

encourage you to go out and do your own fishing for men.

2. *Group Activity:* This week plan a "PIE night" (Pizza, Intercession, and Evangelism). Meet as a group on a Friday night for a big slice of pizza, pray together for 15–20 minutes, then hit the streets or a mall to seek the lost. To make it easier to begin conversations, you may want to use our "Intelligence Test" Survey Tract, which will break the ice and make the transition to spiritual things. If you're bold, you can then witness to the person as they answer the spiritual questions. However, if you're shy (or the person is in a hurry), you can merely say, "Thanks for answering," hand them the survey page, and tell them, "The answers are on the back." There they will find a complete gospel message.

Be sure to take time to share your experiences afterward, to encourage each other and pray for the seeds that were planted.

For Deeper Study

1. Read Luke 16:19–31. Based on these verses, how could you respond to someone who believes there is no conscious existence after death?

2. Some people dismiss the thought of hell by joking, "I don't mind going to hell. All my friends will be there." Rather than a fun, hedonistic place, what will they find instead?

Daniel 12:2

Words of Encouragement

I have been a pastor for 25 years, and always thought I was doing a reasonably good job. Kind of like the folks who consider themselves "good people." I had tried to preach what I thought was the whole counsel of God. I prayed over the years with many people to accept Jesus and make Him Lord of their lives.

About six years ago...I was convicted that something was horribly wrong with my ministry. That night I had the most terrifying, realistic, blood-chilling nightmare any man has ever had. I am a Vietnam veteran and I know a little about nightmares. Nothing in my experience has ever come close to, nor do I ever want it to, the horror of that night!

I dreamed that it was Judgment Day and I was standing next to the throne of God. To my left and my right were pastors as far as I could see. I thought it was odd that the Lord would reserve this front row space for pastors only.

I looked out and saw millions, maybe billions, of people, yet I could see each of their eyes staring at me. As I studied this group I noticed that I knew many of them from times at the altar or ones who had sat under my teaching. I was pleased to see they had made it to heaven, but confused because they didn't look happy. They looked very angry and hateful.

Then I heard the voice of the Lord say, "Away, I never knew you." I was suddenly frightened that what I was seeing was those who *thought* they were saved. I saw all of them pointing a finger at each of us pastors and saying together, in one voice that shook my soul, *"We sat in your church and thought we were saved. Why didn't you tell us we were lost?"*

Tears were pouring down my face and the faces of all of those pastors. I watched as one by one those people were cast into hell. One and then another, and another, and another...., until they were all gone. I died inside as each one screamed in agony and gnashed their teeth, cursing us as they went into the lake of fire.

Then I was looking into the face of Jesus and He said to me, "Is this the part where I'm supposed to say, 'Well done, My good and faithful servant'?" I woke up with a scream and my heart pounding and I was begging Jesus to forgive me.

I died a million deaths that night. Since that night I have done two things on a daily basis. I do everything I can to preach the Law before grace in the hope that conviction of sin will bring a sinner to true salvation. The other thing that I do is pray for every person I have ever preached to, asking God to repair any damage I have done. I also never believe anyone when they tell me they are saved. It is my duty to challenge them and search out the solidness of their salvation.

I have seen several people saved, who thought they were saved, as I have used The Way of the Master material to teach them evangelism.

I do want to hear those words, "Well done, My good and faithful servant," and thanks to you and your team I have a better chance of hearing them. Thank you! I just wanted to let you know, some pastors are waking up to the truth. The desire of my heart is to please God. I pray that my days of being a manpleaser are over along with the nightmares. I also pray that God will use me to bring other pastors into the truth of the gospel message so that they will not have to face the nightmare that I did.

—Steve K., Texas

Matthew 8:12

Romans 2:8,9

Jude 13

What word is repeated four times in Luke 16:23–28?

Did the rich man want his loved ones to join him there?

3. Knowing how his brothers lived, where did the rich man assume they would go? What was needed to change their destination (see Luke 16:30)?

4. No one in his right mind would willingly put his hand on a hot stove, much less walk into a fiery furnace. Yet many flippantly say they won't mind going to hell—where they'll endure agonizing pain for eternity. How can these verses help you to describe the reality of hell to them?

Matthew 13:41,42

Matthew 25:46

Jude 7

Revelation 14:10,11

5. Jesus, whose example we are to follow, spoke more about hell than about heaven. What dire warnings did He give about hell?

Matthew 18:8,9

Luke 12:4,5

MEMORY VERSE

"If your right eye causes you to sin, pluck it out and cast it from you; for it is more profitable for you that one of your members perish, than for your whole body to be cast into hell."

MATTHEW 5:29

LESSON 3
Learning to Share With Loved Ones

SHARE YOUR EXPERIENCES

Briefly discuss the results of the previous lesson's home-work assignment. If you've spoken with strangers, are you ready for the scariest encounters of all—your relatives? Have you ever tried to witness to a family member? Were you fearful? How did it go? Why do you think it is so difficult to speak with people in your family about God?

POINT TO PONDER

We can certainly identify with you if you find the thought of witnessing to a family member awkward or even fearful. There are certain people we would rather not witness to, not because we don't love them, but because we don't want to offend them. Take a moment to list the names of your closest relatives—the ones who are dear to you. Then write down the date you think they're going to die. You say, "I can't do that because I don't know when they're going to die!" Then doesn't that make their salvation even more important? Are there people you love whom you've never witnessed to because you're afraid of losing their favor? If you don't witness to them, you may lose them forever.

Look closely at the words of Jesus on this subject. Read them through twice, so it's clear what He is saying:

"Therefore whoever confesses Me before men, him I will also confess before My Father who is in heaven. But whoever denies Me before men, him I will also deny before My Father who is in heaven. Do not think that I came to bring peace on earth. I did not come to bring peace but a sword. For I have come to 'set a man against his father, a daughter against her mother, and a daughter-in-law against her mother-in-law.' And 'a man's foes will be those of his own household.' He who loves father or mother more than Me is not worthy of Me. And he who loves son or daughter more than Me is not worthy of Me. And he who does not take his cross and follow after Me is not worthy of Me" (Matthew 10:32–38).

Think of Jesus' words, and then think of your worse-case scenario. Imagine if you witness to your family members and you become their enemy. It is as though there is a sword of division between you and those you love. That would be no surprise to you because Jesus said it would happen. But more than likely, your loved ones will politely listen to you and perhaps just write you off as a religious black sheep of the family. But if you love them, you will bear that reproach and continue to pray for them. Believe for the day that your loved ones will get saved. In the meantime, you will have the knowledge that you've done the right thing in speaking to them.

VIEW THE VIDEO Learning to Share With Loved Ones (31 minutes)

Apply the Principles

1. Identify six keys to reaching a loved one.
2. Of the six keys, which do you think you could do to reach a family member?
3. What is a good, non-confrontational approach to use when witnessing to loved ones?

4. Why should we be rich in good works?

5. Name some good works that you are (or could be) doing for your loved ones.

6. What are three principles you could follow to help bring your children to Christ?

7. Name the Ten Commandments, identifying the memory aid for each one.

8. What can you do if your family won't listen to you as you try to share your faith?

QUALITY QUOTE

▶ *Leader's Note: Read this confession with tenderness and sincerity.*

"There was a day when I died, utterly died—died to George Mueller, his opinions, preferences, tastes, and will; died to the world, its approval or censure; died to the approval or blame even of my brethren and friends—and since then I have only to show myself approved to God."
—*George Mueller*

PREACHER'S PROGRESS

The characters: Christian and Telly Marketer
Scene setting: Christian answers the phone. It's a telemarketer. Christian seizes the opportunity to share the gospel with this stranger.

Telly Marketer: "Hello, Mr. Christian. How are you? I wonder if I could have just one moment of your time. We want to offer you a subscription to *Sports Ill-Lustrated* with the special 'Swimsuit Issue.' If you subscribe, we will give you a chance to win a free trip for two to Hawaii, beer for a year, or a new car. We will also give you, absolutely free of charge, a brand new duffel bag with your favorite sports hero's picture on it. How would you like to pay for your subscription—with a Visa or MasterCard?"

Christian: "May I ask you a question?"

Telly Marketer: "Certainly, Mr. Christian. I would be happy to answer any of your questions."

Christian: "What do you think happens when a person dies?"

Telly Marketer: "Um ... I'm afraid I don't have that information on my screen. Are there any other questions I can help you with?"

Christian: "Yes. Would you consider yourself to be a good person?"

Telly Marketer: "Huh?"

Christian: "Have you kept the Ten Commandments?"

Telly Marketer: "I think I've kept most of them."

Christian: "Have you ever lied?"

Telly Marketer: "Yes, Mr. Christian. I have to admit that I have told a few fibs and white lies, but that was long ago."

Christian: "What does that make you?"

Telly Marketer: "It doesn't make me anything."

Christian: "If I told a lie, what would I be called?"

Telly Marketer: "A liar, I guess."

Christian: "So what are you?"

Telly Marketer: "Technically, I'm a liar. But that was in the past."

Christian: "Sure. Everything is in the past. Have you ever stolen something, even if it's small?"

Telly Marketer: "Yes, sir."

Christian: "What does that make you?"

Telly Marketer: "A thief."

Christian: "Jesus said that if you look with lust, you've already committed adultery with that person in your heart. Have you ever looked with lust?"

Telly Marketer: "Many times."

Christian: "If God were to judge you by the Ten Commandments on Judgment Day, would you be innocent or guilty?"

Telly Marketer: "I suppose I would be guilty."

Christian: "Would you go to heaven or hell?"

Telly Marketer: "Hell…"

Telemarketers are a good way for you to practice what you preach. You don't have to look them in the eye. You can't be injured by them. The worst thing they can do is hang up in your ear. If that happens, you can rejoice that they were convicted enough to do so. You not only had the privilege of planting the seed of God's Word in the heart of a stranger, but you proved yourself to be faithful to the Lord, you conquered the fear of man, and now you can rejoice that you were rejected for the sake of righteousness. If they hang up, spend a moment in prayer for them. If they are open to hearing more, take them through the cross, repentance, and faith. Ask if they have a Bible at home, encourage them to read it daily, and then thank them for listening to you.

CLOSE IN PRAYER

Break Out of Your Comfort Zone

1. *Individual Activity:* If you have unsaved family members or close friends, write them a letter expressing your concern for their eternal welfare, or record an audio message as suggested in the "Words of Encouragement." They don't have to live far away. Even if they live in your town, it's sometimes more effective to let them hear your concern and the gospel message when they're alone and in the privacy of their own home. They may be more receptive and less defensive if they can reflect on your words and not feel compelled to immediately respond face to face. Bathe it in prayer, then let the Holy Spirit give you the words to say.

   If you don't have any unsaved family or friends, here's something you can do to reach strangers. Run a small classified ad in your local newspaper, pointing people to the truth of the gospel. If your paper doesn't have an Announcement section where notices can be run for free, skip the Starbuck's coffee this week and invest those dollars in something with eternal value instead by buying an ad. Here's some suggested wording:

   > Would you consider yourself to be a good person? Good enough to go to heaven? Are you sure? Eternity is a long time to be wrong. Find out at www.needgod.com.

   > The gospel message at www.needgod.com is very simple and straightforward, and presents unbelievers with a simple eight-question "test" to see if they are good enough to get into heaven.

2. *Group Activity:* Set a time this week to go to a local amusement park, sports event (including high school or college games), or anywhere large crowds can be found. If there are no special events in your area, go to the local mall. Share the gospel with those who are gathered there, hand out tracts, and don't forget to place tracts on car windshields before you leave. The larger the crowd, the more seeds that can be planted. Then pray for those seeds to grow!

For Deeper Study

1. Keeping in mind that God loves your family members even more than you do, how can you avoid discouragement in trying to reach them? (See 1 Timothy 2:4; 2 Peter 3:9.)

2. How can you encourage your loved ones to think seriously about the things of eternity? (See 2 Corinthians 6:2; James 4:13,14.)

3. Be careful not to pressure your family members into making a decision. Salvation is of the Lord (see Jonah 2:9), so what must we rely on God to do, according to the following verses?

John 6:44

1 Timothy 2:7

Words of Encouragement

I have been wanting to witness to my 86-year-old grandpa for a long time. He lives a couple of hours away from me and we do not have a very close relationship, yet I see him a few times a year and send him cards in the mail. This year as his birthday approached I was thinking hard about what I could do for him. He has a very hard heart and my parents have tried witnessing to him a few times this year and he did not take it well at all. I knew a phone call was not the route to go, and he is not a reader so a letter would not do either.

I decided to make a cassette of me sending him a "birthday message." I started in the natural and talked about how long he has lived and how I was proud to be a part of his big family, and then I swung it to the spiritual and shared the Ten Commandments and the realities of hell and what the Bible says about it. (My parents told me he said he wasn't afraid of hell because he just believed he would cease to exist when he dies.)

I was able to sit and go through the Law and the gospel and plead with him about the realities of the Bible—all in a relaxed atmosphere knowing I could always stop and rewind and start over if I felt I was messing up. I didn't have to do that, though. My first try the Holy Spirit really helped me with the right words.

I am going to start doing this for other family members and friends who live far away and have been on my heart. What a great way to share the gospel in a personal way, and I really think people will appreciate the time taken to do that. It's also nice for those of us who are new at sharing our faith.

—*Kim S.*

John 16:8

2 Timothy 2:25

4. In addition to sharing the gospel verbally at least one time, what else can we do to help lead our loved ones to the Lord?

Matthew 5:16

1 Timothy 6:18

Titus 2:6–8

1 Peter 3:1,2

5. To raise godly children, the first step is to ensure you're a godly example. Scripture gives us a good picture of a godly person. Read Psalm 1:1–3, and write down its conditions and promises.

6. Luke 8:39 tells us, "Return to your own house, and tell what great things God has done for you." It may be best to speak to your loved ones from your own perspective, telling them how you came to know you needed a Savior. Write down your personal testimony, being sure to mention the Moral Law and the penalty for breaking it.

LESSON 4
Pressing On When Things Go Wrong

OPEN IN PRAYER

SHARE YOUR EXPERIENCES

Briefly discuss the results of the previous lesson's home-work assignment. What are some of your fears when it comes to witnessing? Is it a fear of failure? What has been your greatest failure when witnessing? Looking back, was that a negative or positive experience?

POINT TO PONDER

Most of us are fearful of failure. We shouldn't be, though, because that fear can destroy one unique and important ability that God has given you—that is, to be "creative." You have been made in the image of the Creator, and He has given you abilities that He didn't give the rest of crea-tion. Dogs and cats can't create beautiful music, or invent, or reason the way human beings can. Some of the most creative men and women in history were close friends of failure. They *lived* with failure because they understood that it was part of the discovery process. Edison left a trail of failed attempts on his way to inventing the light bulb, and failure is part of the lives of those of us who want to let our light shine in this dark world.

Ray recently received a phone call from a woman in Australia, who said that twenty years earlier, she had been running along a beach in New Zealand when Ray ran alongside her and witnessed to her. Although she had ridiculed him at the time, shortly afterward she was soundly saved. Since then, she has led half of her family to Christ, including her father on his deathbed. And now she and her husband travel together and preach the gospel.

So if you are ridiculed for sharing your faith, or have a disastrous experience and feel like a failure, don't spend too long licking your wounds. Think of it like this. A young boy is learning to ride his bike. As he begins to earnestly peddle, his father deliberately lets go. The boy rides on his own for a moment, then falls to the ground and hurts himself as he thuds onto the grass. Imagine if he then turns to his father and says, 'You betrayed me! You let me go by myself. I will *never* get on that bike again.' Will that father say, 'Okay, son. Who cares that you never learn to ride a bike'? Of course not. As his loving father, he will encourage him by firmly saying, 'Son, that pain will actually work for you. It will give you built-in knowledge and valuable experience for the future. Now get back on the bike, and you will be riding before you know it.'"

Never be discouraged. God promises to work all things out for good (see Romans 8:28). Now get back on the bike, and let that painful experience work for you, so that you can be even more effective in reaching the lost. There's no such thing as failure, when you are faithful.

VIEW THE VIDEO **Pressing On When Things Go Wrong (30 minutes)**

Apply the Principles

1. Why was this episode filmed in a boxing ring?
2. Have you ever been persecuted for your faith?

3. If you haven't been persecuted, should you be (in light of 2 Timothy 3:12)?

4. Do you ever feel discouraged by negative reactions to the gospel? Why?

5. Should Christians allow themselves to be discouraged? Why or why not?

6. Why does the world hate Christians?

7. What happened to Paul as he preached the biblical gospel?

8. What does the enemy use to discourage you from sharing your faith?

9. What is the antidote to discouragement?

QUALITY QUOTE

▶ *Leader's Note: Preach this one with conviction to your fellow "soldiers in training."*

A barracks is meant to be a place where real soldiers are to be fed and equipped for war, not a place to settle down in or as a comfortable snuggery in which to enjoy ourselves. I hope that if ever they, our soldiers, do settle down God will burn their barracks over their heads!

—*Catherine Booth (co-founder of the Salvation Army)*

PREACHER'S PROGRESS

The characters: Christian and Lucy Mouth
Scene setting: Lucy Mouth is listening in on Christian's conversation with Sal (from Lesson 2), and decides to argue.

Lucy Mouth: "I heard what you said to Sal. I haven't made a #!*$ god to suit myself. And I don't believe in heaven or hell."

Christian: "May I ask you a few questions?"

Lucy Mouth: "Sure."

Christian: "Have you ever used God's name in vain?"

Lucy Mouth: "What do you mean?"

Christian: "Have you ever used God's name as a cuss word? You know… when something goes wrong, you say, 'Oh, G-d!'"

Lucy Mouth: "Yeah, I've done that, plenty of times. So what?"

Christian: "Do you know what you are doing when you do that?"

Lucy Mouth: "No. And I don't *!#&$ care."

Christian: "Let me tell you what you are doing. Instead of saying a filth word beginning with 's' to express disgust, you are taking the holy name of the God who gave you life and using it as a substitute to express your disgust."

Lucy Mouth: "I don't believe in a #@$!* God."

Christian: "That doesn't matter. You still have to face Him on Judgment Day whether you believe in Him or not. What you've done is called blasphemy, and the Bible says, 'The Lord will not hold him guiltless who takes His name in vain.' God gave you a conscience. You know right from wrong… and I wouldn't be in your shoes on Judgment Day for all the tea in China. But thanks for listening to me. Bye."

Never be afraid to be (lovingly) confrontational. You will be amazed at what you can say to someone if your tone is in the right spirit of gentleness. And don't be afraid to use fear as a motivator. Any fear a person has now because of your words of warning will be nothing compared to the fear he will have if he "falls into the hands of the living God." The lake of fire should motivate the Christian to cast aside his own fear of rejection that can come in the guise of not wanting to offend the unbeliever.

CLOSE IN PRAYER

Break Out of Your Comfort Zone

1. *Individual Activity:* Are you ready to be stretched? Do you care enough about the fate of unsaved people to do something radical to reach them? You've been given a way to share the gospel that was unavailable to Christians for more than nineteen hundred years—a way that doesn't require you to put your life on the line, or even look a stranger in the eye. It uses a special book containing the names and phone numbers of many unsaved people. It's the phone book. Here's what to do. Call three people and conduct a "phone survey." Just dial a number and say, "Hello. My name is _____. I'm not selling anything. I'm working with WOTM Radio [it's on Sirius Satellite Radio], doing a simple three-question survey to find out about America's spirituality. Do you have a few moments to answer some questions?" The worst that can happen is that they hang up or say no. Or they may say, "Sure." Ask:

   1. Do you consider yourself to be a morally good person?

   2. Do you think you've kept the Ten Commandments?

   3. How many have you actually kept? For instance, have you ever lied? Stolen? Blasphemed? etc.

   Then say, "Thanks for answering those. That's the end of the survey. That was easy, wasn't it? May I have your first name? So, Elizabeth, how do you think you will do on Judgment Day—if God judges you by the Ten Commandments, do you think you will be innocent or guilty? Do you think you would go to heaven or hell? Does that concern you? (etc.)" We regularly do this live on Way of the Master Radio, and you would be amazed at how many people want to talk about their beliefs.

Once you have your results, you can send them to us at comments@WayoftheMasterRadio.com.

2. *Group Activity:* Follow Jesus' model in Luke 10:1 and send your fishing team out two-by-two into the community, to go door-to-door evangelizing. You can use the same three questions above, or use our "Intelligence Test" Survey Tract to guide your conversation. Don't worry about being nervous when you start, but after the first few homes expect to be pumped up for evangelism and not want to stop. Simply tell people you're from a local church and are conducting a survey to see what people in your community believe.

   In most cases, the majority of people who answer the door agree to take the survey and will let you present the gospel. Then thank them for taking the survey, leave them with a tract (such as "Are You a Good Person?"), and offer them a New Testament if they don't have one in the house already. Doing this will give the fainthearted a boost in faith. Not convinced? Read this testimony:

   > I listen to your broadcast every day by way of podcast. Some friends of mine and I have become involved in witnessing over the last year due in large part to the Way of the Master series and program. Saturday morning we went out door-to-door in the poorer areas of Milwaukee. As we canvassed I have never heard as many say, "I have never heard the gospel put like that before." We don't get to, nor do we have to, know if the people we spoke to received God's gift of salvation but God has renewed and restored once again the fire and the passion to "go." After talking among ourselves after the excursion, we agreed that this was the "joy" and "abundant life" that the Bible refers to! —*Michael D., Wisconsin*

   Another great way to quickly get people's attention is to begin by offering to do small handyman chores for free, then ask if you can conduct a quick survey. Offer this only when you have volunteers available to do what you promise! Few people will actually take you up on your offer, but your willingness to do so speaks volumes. For more details on how to do this, see Appendix B.

Words of Encouragement

I asked God to place such a burden on my heart to evangelize that my life would be a wreck unless I started to get out and do it. I'm consumed with evangelism!

I went to one of the toughest areas in town, and began to street evangelize. It went AWESOME! One guy tried to run me over with his scooter! He was the hardest looking one of the bunch. He had tattoos up and down his arms, used rotten language, and had been in prison most of his life. He approached as if he was going to strike me in the face. I bounced back to the "natural" and asked him about his muscles and if he was in good health. He calmed down and laughed, "I'm getting very fat." I asked, "Do you mind if I check how well your spiritual health is?" He said, "Sure." I began to go through the Ten Commandments with him. He confessed his guilt to all of them! He was absolutely crushed under the Law! He became contrite, and very nice. Tears began to well up in his eyes when he found out he was guilty before a Righteous Judge and knew his fate was everlasting torment in the lake of fire.

I then told him about what Jesus had done for him so he wouldn't have to go to hell, if only he would repent and turn from his sinful ways, and put his faith in the Savior. I gave him a tract, which he nearly jerked my arm out of its socket to get! I asked if I could pray with him, and he said YES! I prayed with him, and he began to transform right before my eyes! WOW! He rode off proclaiming what Jesus did for him so he wouldn't have to go to hell, to all who were standing around. What a day! I will never give up.

—*Jeff R., Arizona*

For Deeper Study

1. It would be nice if we could talk about the need for a Savior and still be well liked by the world. But what does the Bible tell us we should expect regarding difficulties and persecution?

   John 15:19–21

   1 Thessalonians 3:3,4

   1 Peter 4:12,13

2. It's crucial that we maintain the right perspective when witnessing, so we don't give up. If we're rejected because of our witness, why should it be a cause for encouragement rather than discouragement?

   Luke 6:22–23

   Philippians 1:12,13

   1 Peter 3:14–16

1 Peter 4:14

3. In order to "fight the good fight of faith" (1 Timothy 6:12), it's essential that we not enter the ring unprepared. What should we do to be properly trained?

2 Timothy 2:3–5

2 Timothy 2:15

Hebrews 12:1,2

4. The message we speak can be offensive by itself. How can we ensure we don't offend people by our delivery but always "speak the truth in love"?

2 Timothy 2:24–26

Titus 3:1–3

5. Regardless of how people receive our message, we can have confidence that God's Word will not return void (see Isaiah 55:11). According to 2 Timothy 4:2–5, what are we to be faithful to do?

LESSON 5
Giving Hope to Those Who Are Gay

OPEN IN PRAYER

SHARE YOUR EXPERIENCES

Briefly discuss the results of the previous lesson's homework assignment. How did your surveys go?

If you've ever witnessed to someone who is gay, were you more nervous than usual? Why? How did you handle it? What was your greatest fear?

POINT TO PONDER

If I offered you a fistful of diamonds or a glass of cold water right now, which would you take? The diamonds, of course—who in his right mind wouldn't? But if you were crawling through a desert with blistered lips and a swollen tongue, dying of thirst, and I offered you a fistful of diamonds or a glass of cold water, you would despise the diamonds and cry, "Give me water—or I'll die!" That is called "circumstantial priorities." Your priorities change according to your circumstances.

Christianity demands a choice between the sparkling diamonds of sin and the cool, clear water of everlasting life. Most people prefer the diamonds of sin, something quite normal for sin-loving humanity. But on Judgment Day their circumstances will radically change. They will find themselves upon their faces in the desert of God's judgment, about to perish under the burning heat of a Creator who warns us that He is a "consuming fire." They despised the Living Water when it was offered to them in Christ. Now they must face eternal consequences. Those sparkling diamonds they so dearly clutch will suddenly be the glaring evidence for their condemnation. (From *The Evidence Bible*, Bridge-Logos Publishers)

VIEW THE VIDEO Giving Hope to Those Who Are Gay (31 minutes)

Apply the Principles

1. Do you think some Christians are condescending toward homosexuals? If so, why do you think this is?

2. Identify two Bible verses that make it clear that homosexuality is morally wrong.

3. How would you answer a homosexual who says that he was "born that way"?

4. From where should we get our moral guide—our feelings or God's Word?

5. What is a good response when someone says you're "homophobic"?

6. What Scripture tells us that the Law was made for homosexuals? Why is this?

7. When should you talk to a homosexual about homosexuality being a sin?

8. Would you find it comfortable witnessing to a homosexual? Why or why not?

QUALITY QUOTE

▶ *Leader's Note: Remember, don't just read this, preach it! Be Charles Spurgeon, the Prince of Preachers, preaching to a crowd that is hungry to hear some truth!*

> The Law reveals the exceeding abundance of sin, *by revealing to us the depravity of our nature.* We are all prepared to charge the serpent with our guilt or to insinuate that we go astray from the force of ill example—but the Holy Spirit dissipates these dreams by bringing the Law into the heart. Then the fountains of the great deep are broken up, the chambers of the imagery are opened, and the innate evil of the very essence of fallen man is discovered.
> —*Charles Spurgeon*

PREACHER'S PROGRESS

The characters: Christian and Ben Gay
Scene setting: Christian is out sharing the gospel and encounters a homosexual, Ben Gay.

Ben Gay: "Hey, Christian, I'm gay, and science has proved that I was born like this."

Christian: "True. I was born like that too."

Ben Gay: "Huh?"

Christian: "I was also born with a tendency to lie, steal, commit adultery, and sleep around. It's called 'sin' and it's in every one of us."

Ben Gay: "So are you saying that I'm going to hell just because I'm homosexual?"

Christian: "I didn't even mention hell. Where do you think you will go when you die?"

Ben Gay: "Heaven."

Christian: "Why?"

Ben Gay: "Because I'm a good person."

Christian: "Do you want to take a quick test to see if you are?"

Ben Gay: "Sure."

Christian: "Have you ever told a lie? Stolen? Used God's name in vain?" (etc.)

The Bible tells us that the Moral Law was made for homosexuals (see 1 Timothy 1:8–10). If you use the Law when witnessing, you won't even have to mention their sexual preference, and thus be accused of "hate" and "prejudice." The Law will show the homosexual that he is condemned regardless of his sexual preference. When he finds a place of true repentance and faith in Jesus, God will take away his unclean spirit and give him a new heart with new desires and the power to obey the truth of God's Word.

CLOSE IN PRAYER

Break Out of Your Comfort Zone

1. *Individual Activity:* For an easy way to sow seeds of the gospel, take time this week to visit your local library. Browse through books in the sections on other religions (such as Hinduism, Mormonism, New Age), atheism, astrology, etc., and slip in a gospel tract for the next reader to find. The Million Dollar Bill, Intelligence Test bookmark, and Good News & Bad News tracts are eye-catching and don't fall out easily.

    While you're there, use the library computer to go to www.areyouagoodperson.org, and leave the opening screen displayed.

2. *Group Activity:* Select a gas station located at a busy intersection, and ask if you can hold a car wash there. Offering a free service is a good way to get people's attention, and in washing

their car you'll give recipients about 10 minutes of time to kill. Make good use of that time by sharing the gospel with them while they're waiting. To advertise your car wash, have a couple of people standing at the street corners holding signs, but don't mention your church name on the sign. Almost without exception, people will ask you why you're doing this, so you can explain that you want to give back to the community, and to talk to people and find out if they have any spiritual beliefs. People are usually pretty open and happy to tell you what their beliefs are. Take them through the "Good Person" test, and leave them with a tract.

This is a good way to involve others in your church in your outreach efforts. They may not feel comfortable sharing their faith just yet, but there are probably several who could lend a hand in washing cars while you speak to people. Perhaps they will see how easy it is, and be inspired to join you.

For Deeper Study

1. Homosexuals claim their desires are natural and therefore acceptable. What does God's Word say about this in the following verses?

Matthew 19:4,5

Romans 1:26,27

Ephesians 2:1–3

Proverbs 14:12

Words of Encouragement

I had first accepted Christ when I was 16. However, homosexuality kept me depressed spiritually for about 40 years. I am now doing very well living for God by the power of His Holy Spirit and by allowing His Word to heal me spiritually. My communication with God in prayer and worship both privately and corporately is a mainstay in my daily life. I am now walking the steps of a righteous man and I owe it all to my Lord and Savior Jesus Christ. I am no novice to the tricks of the devil to deceive and to tempt, and am trusting in God's Word to keep me daily.

I have watched your TV show when you have interviewed gay men on the street. God bless you for being compassionate enough in Christ to do that. Please don't give up on the lost and deceived homosexuals, because no matter how far away any seem, God's Word is the light and power they all need to come on out and experience God's help. I can't tell you the times I thought all was hopeless. However, God never allowed me to buy all the way into the deception that "I was born that way" or "God made me that way," etc.

Anyway, I continue to thank God for your life and ministry and to pray for you, your families, and your ministry.

—Bob K., New Mexico

2. According to the following verses, what will happen to those who give in to these sinful desires?

Romans 1:26,27

Jude 7

3. Read Romans 1:29–32. To keep Christians from pinpointing homosexual behavior, what other traits does this passage say are deserving of God's judgment?

How many of these traits were true of you before you came to Christ?

4. What hope do these verses offer that people can be delivered from a homosexual lifestyle?

Ezekiel 18:30–32

1 Corinthians 6:9–11

1 Corinthians 10:13

Titus 3:3–6

LESSON 6
Recognizing Satanic Influence

OPEN IN PRAYER

SHARE YOUR EXPERIENCES

Briefly discuss any witnessing encounters you've had in the last week. What is the most important thing you have learned so far in this course?

POINT TO PONDER

John Wesley (the famous preacher who regularly rode on horseback for hundreds of miles to reach the lost and preached in the open air to multitudes) once conducted an experiment that is extremely interesting. It was June 8, 1740. He said, "For these two days I had made an experiment which I had so often and earnestly been pressed to do— speaking to none concerning the things of God unless my heart was free to it."[1] In other words, he decided not to witness unless he *felt* like doing it. He then related the result of this experiment: 1) He rode in a horse-drawn carriage for 80 miles without witnessing to a soul, except for a few superficial words of greeting. 2) He had no cross to bear or take up (he didn't feel like a "religious weirdo") and

---

1 *The Journal of John Wesley* (Chicago, IL: Moody Press, 1939), p. 90.

fell asleep for two hours. 3) He had much respect shown to him, and was considered "a civil, good-natured gentleman."

Then he lamented, "Oh, how pleasing is all this to flesh and blood! Need ye 'compass sea and land' to make 'proselytes' to this?" In other words, using the words of Jesus when He called a particular convert "a child of hell" (Matthew 23:15)—is this what we are supposed to be?

If we care about the unsaved, we must *make* ourselves speak to them. If we go by our "feelings," we will always take the low road of the world's approval. To witness for Christ means a continual denial of self, of comfort, and of wanting worldly respect. It means bearing the reproach of the cross. Charles Spurgeon so rightly said, "We must school and train ourselves to deal personally with the unconverted. We must not excuse ourselves, but force ourselves to the irksome task until it becomes easy."

And even when we become so adept that sharing the gospel is second nature, we can never wait until we *feel* like it. That never happens. No sane firefighter waits for his feelings to tell him to brave the flames. His feelings tell him to stay in the truck because he knows that he could get horribly burned. He risks his life to rescue victims not because of his "feelings," but because of his continual resolute firefighting mindset. It's his responsibility.

VIEW THE VIDEO Recognizing Satanic Influence (30 minutes)

Apply the Principles

1. Do you think Satan has any influence on heavy metal rock music?

2. Do you think that sort of music carries a message? If so, what is it?

3. How does Scripture describe Satan?

4. Do you think the average person believes there is such a thing as "evil"? What about a literal devil?

5. What were your beliefs in this respect, before you were converted?

6. Do you think someone can be genuinely saved and yet deny the existence of Satan?

7. What is the main message of the Satanic Bible? How has this same mindset infiltrated the church?

8. Explain how the modern gospel distorts the picture given in the parable of the Prodigal Son.

9. Why do you think so many professed Christians are more concerned about what they can get from God than what they can do for Him?

QUALITY QUOTE

▶ *Leader's Note: Read this sobering thought slowly and with conviction.*

Satan, the god of all dissension, stirreth up daily new sects, and last of all (which of all other I should never have foreseen or once suspected), he has raised up a sect such as teach that the Ten Commandments ought to be taken out of the church, and that men should not be terrified by the Law, but gently exhorted by the preaching of the grace of Christ.
—*Martin Luther*

PREACHER'S PROGRESS

The characters: Christian and Ian Oculated
Scene setting: Christian and Ian are sitting on a bench after playing a basketball game together.

Ian Oculated: "I know what you are saying is true."

Christian: "Good."

Ian Oculated: "I gave my heart to Jesus when I was 14 years old."

Christian: "Where was that?"

Ian Oculated: "At a Christian rock music crusade. Some guy at the end said that Jesus loved us, so I went up to the front with some friends."

Christian: "Did you repent?"

Ian Oculated: "I don't know about that; but I became involved in a youth group for a while. Then I got mixed up with this girl and we... well, you know what I mean. I'm not going to any church at the moment, but I still love God."

Christian: "Do you know that if you are not trusting in Jesus, you are an enemy of God in your mind through wicked works?"

Ian Oculated: "I don't believe that. I do believe that God loves me... and I have been born again, and that's all that matters."

Christian: "Are you living in holiness? The Bible says, 'Without holiness, no man will see the Lord.'"

Ian Oculated: "Yes."

Christian: "What is holiness?"

Ian Oculated: "Ah... I don't really know."

Christian: "Are you reading your Bible?"

Ian Oculated: "Sometimes."

Christian: "Would you consider yourself to be a good person?"

Ian Oculated: "Of course."

Christian: "Let's see. We'll look for a moment at the Ten Commandments and see how you will do on Judgment Day. Okay?"

Ian Oculated: "Okay…"

CLOSE IN PRAYER

Break Out of Your Comfort Zone

1. *Individual Activity:* Here's an easy way to get a nibble when fishing, without even trying. It's like sitting in the boat, going about your activities, when there's a tug on the line—someone has taken the bait. Just make a button that says "Do you consider yourself to be a good person?" and wear it when you go out. It's as easy as putting a worm on a hook.

   If you feel bold, you can point it out and begin a conversation. If you're not so bold, people will still bite. Don't be surprised if you hear someone say, "I was reading your button and yes, I think I'm a good person!" If you don't have time to start a conversation, hand the person the booklet "Are You a Good Person?" and explain, "Well, here's a test you can take to see if you really are good."

   You should be able to find a button design kit at a local craft store, so you can print your message and snap it in the plastic button. Or, you can also buy ready-made buttons at www.cafepress.com/livingwaterscom/274739.

2. *Group Activity:* Plan another group fishing trip, but this time bring a video camera along to film your conversations. Just as many people are motivated by watching Ray and Kirk witnessing on the videos, people in your church will be encouraged and inspired by seeing some of their own out boldly sharing their faith. Read this letter we received:

We have been studying "Hell's Best Kept Secret" at our church and I kept hearing people say, "Normal people couldn't do that like Ray and Kirk do." So another member and I decided to make our own "way of the Master" video and show the church that truly anyone could walk up to a stranger and witness using this method. We went to Indiana University and just began to walk the campus and talk to people. It was so easy and a very wonderful experience. In a two-hour period we were able to witness to a Muslim, a Buddhist, two Jewish girls who claimed that Jews did not believe in the Ten Commandments, a Mormon student, and two atheists. We were just so encouraged that we were able share our faith with these people... Thank you for being so faithful and for teaching me how to truly witness to someone without just inviting them to go to church with me.
—*Craig H., Indiana*

Anyone who has a heart for the lost can do it! Again, asking others in the church to help by doing the filming will let them see that this isn't as scary as it sounds. Once your footage is filmed, ask the pastor if you can show it to the church and encourage others to go through the training course, so they can follow your example as you follow Christ.

DON'T MISS WOTM RADIO!

As you are listening to The Way of the Master Radio (available daily), why not encourage others in your church to tune in at **www.WayoftheMasterRadio.com**?

"Never stop what you are doing!!! Never stop your radio ministry. Never stop giving live examples of witnessing encounters. I hear them, and I see them, and I AM CONVICTED!!!!!! I am listening, learning, and using these materials for an effective and bold witness. The mere act of hearing people being witnessed to and their responses brings me to tears. Whether they accept or refuse the gospel, they make a decision and either way my heart weeps. My body trembles. My soul is renewed daily by the reading of the Word and the witness of your example.[2] Thank you for running. Thank you for fighting. Thank you for carrying the torch. I'm right beside you as you fuel me up."
—*Kenric T.*

---

2 For more incredible real-life witnessing encounters, don't miss *Thanks a Million* by Ray Comfort and Kirk Cameron (Bridge-Logos Publishers).

For Deeper Study

1. Most people naturally claim that they don't worship or serve Satan. According to the following verses, in what ways can individuals be influenced to do Satan's will without knowing it?

   1 Chronicles 21:1

   John 13:2,27

   Acts 5:3

   1 Corinthians 10:19,20

2. How pervasive is Satan's influence over unbelievers—whether they're aware of it or not?

   John 8:44a

   2 Timothy 2:26

   1 John 5:19

3. Going through the Moral Law will help sinners see how they're reflecting the traits of their father, the devil, and do his will. What family resemblance can be seen if they've broken the following Commandments?

If they've ever told a lie (see John 8:44c)

If they've stolen anything (see John 10:10)

If they've hated anyone (see John 8:44b; 10:10)

4. What are the "snares" the devil sets for mankind? Read 1 John 2:16 and list the three categories of temptations.

According to Genesis 3:6, how did Satan tempt Eve (and Adam) in these ways?

Read Luke 4:1–13. How did Satan tempt Jesus in these same ways?

Hebrews 4:15 tells us that Jesus was in points tempted as we are. Yet Jesus, "the last Adam" (1 Corinthians 15:45), was victorious where the first Adam failed. How does Luke say Jesus was able to overcome each temptation?

5. Satan opposes believers and hinders our work. Yet we are "not ignorant of his devices" (2 Corinthians 2:11). What are some of the enemy's tactics?

Genesis 3:1–5

Words of Encouragement

I'm a 19-year-old college student who found your program on TBN one day, and have been hooked ever since. I thought the concept of a "Christian reality TV series" sounded curious—I figured it was just another attempt by the church to imitate the world. Thankfully, it was anything but!

Thanks to learning the real way of the Master, I have been given the confidence to witness to *dozens* of people of all walks of life, on college campus in particular. I have not had a single off-handed rejection or outright refusal, although neither have I had any on-the-spot converts. Most of them are truly convicted, and promise to give some thought to the matter. Will it not be exciting to get to heaven and find out how many are there because Christ used me?! The use of the Law is biblical, and clearly a weapon in the Christian's witnessing arsenal which the devil has mostly managed to remove!

I was speaking with a friend about the doctrine of "once saved, always saved" versus "keep 'maintaining' your salvation, because it's possible to lose it" and it occurred to me, could it be that the false doctrine of "you can lose your salvation" is the result of so many false converts falling away into sin? In other words, so many in the church are not true converts, as Ray has pointed out. Thus, when many fall away into sin and temptation, other believers, believing that the fallen were true believers, can only surmise that you can lose your salvation because look at what happened to this "Christian" brother! It seems this could be one way the devil is propagating this false doctrine.

—*David R., Kentucky*

Acts 13:8–10

2 Corinthians 4:4

2 Corinthians 11:3,4

2 Corinthians 11:13–15

1 Timothy 4:1

6. The only way to avoid deception is to know the truth. Read Acts 26:18. God sent Paul—and each of us—to share the truth with others. How can our obedience rescue the lost from the enemy's grasp?

LESSON 7
Answering Atheism

▶ *Materials Needed: Small piece of paper and pen for each participant*

OPEN IN PRAYER

SHARE YOUR EXPERIENCES

Briefly discuss your witnessing encounters from the last week. What is the worst witnessing experience you have ever had? What is your best? Which experience is easiest to remember?

POINT TO PONDER

Most Christians feel intellectually intimidated when they witness to a professing atheist. This is because we have bought into the lie that atheism and intellectualism are synonymous. The exact opposite is true. The Bible tells us that those who profess to be atheists aren't thinking intelligently when it comes to God; they are fools (Psalm 14:1). It makes far more sense that a man denies the existence of the sun at noon on a cloudless day than it does for him to deny the existence of God. In today's lesson you will see a unique way to humble an atheist (or any proud person).

▶ *Leader's Note: Hand out paper and pens to participants. As you ask the following five questions out loud, have participants write their responses. Tell them not to call out any of the answers. THIS IS IMPORTANT. Encourage them to listen carefully, because the questions will not be repeated.*

1. What is the name of the raised print that deaf people use? *(write answer)*
2. How many of each animal did Moses take into the ark? *(write answer)*
3. Spell the word "shop."

▶ *Leader's Note: Have participants answer the first part out loud together, then write the answer to the following question:*

What do you do when you come to a green light? *(write answer)*

4. Listen carefully. You are the driver of a train. There are thirty people on board. At the first stop, ten people get on. At the next stop, five people get off. Now for the question: What is the name of the train driver? *(write answer)*
5. It is noon. You look at the clock. The big hand is on three, and the little hand is on five. What time is it? *(write answer)*

▶ *Leader's Note: The answers can be found on page 86. Read them aloud to participants.*

VIEW THE VIDEO **Answering Atheism (31 minutes)**

Apply the Principles

1. In light of the absurdity of the "evolution" of the soda can, why do you think so many people deny that there is an intelligent Creator?
2. Many claim that there is no proof for God's existence. Is that true?
3. What do you think of the building/builder analogy? What other evidence can you use to prove the existence of God?
4. "There is no God" is an absolute statement. Do you think an atheist can make that statement with intellectual integrity? Why or why not?
5. Why is there no such thing as an atheist?

6. After an atheist begins to backslide (change his mind about God), why is it important to swing from the area of the intellect to the conscience? Did you notice how the backsliding atheist in the video clip was feeling conviction of sin despite his atheistic statements?

7. How can a person find absolute proof of God's existence and the truth of Jesus' words? (See John 7:17; 14:21,23.)

QUALITY QUOTE

▶ *Leader's Note: Read this quote with enthusiasm, to persuade your listeners of its truth.*

Men who never heard the gospel can see God in his works if they open their eyes. There is written upon the face of nature enough to condemn men if they do not turn to God. There is a gospel of the sea, and of the heavens, of the stars, and of the sun; and if men will not read it, they are guilty, for they are willfully ignorant of what they might know, and ought to know.
—*Charles Spurgeon*

PREACHER'S PROGRESS

The characters: Christian and Will Fullyblind
Scene setting: Christian is at a park, talking with a typical atheist named Will.

Will Fullyblind: "I think seeing is believing. If I can't see it, I don't believe it exists."

Christian: "So if there's anything you can't see, you don't believe it exists?"

Will Fullyblind: "That's right."

Christian: "Have you ever seen your brain?"

Will Fullyblind: "No."

Christian: "Doesn't that make you think?"

Will Fullyblind: "Yes."

Christian: "We believe in many things that we can't see. Have you ever seen the wind? Have you seen history? We see the effects of the wind, but the wind is invisible. We have records of history, but it is by 'faith' that we believe certain historical events happened. Television waves are invisible, but an antenna and a receiver can detect their presence. By the way, did you know that you have a receiver?"

Will Fullyblind: "No."

Christian: "Your 'receiver' (your spirit) is dead because of sin [see Ephesians 2:1]. You need to be plugged into the life of God, and then you will come alive and be aware of the invisible spiritual realm. Do you think you have kept the Ten Commandments? . . ."

CLOSE IN PRAYER

Break Out of Your Comfort Zone

1. *Individual Activity:* How did you learn biblical evangelism? More than likely it was from watching someone else. The disciples had Jesus as their personal example. Paul learned from Jesus, and the Church learned from Paul. Do you think you've learned enough to teach someone else? That's the key to reaching this world for the gospel—training up laborers. Go out witnessing this week, and take someone with you who has never shared the gospel. Let that person watch you do it. This may add a little pressure on you, but it is perhaps the best way for the person to learn. Remember when

you moved from simply believing this teaching to actually *experiencing* it in real life? After you do the "heavy lifting" of taking the lost person through the Law, invite this listener to jump in and share the gospel—the good news of Jesus paying the person's fine.

2. *Group Activity:* Most towns have a weekly swap meet or flea market, where you can rent a table for a nominal charge (usually around $10). Rent a table on a Saturday and spend a few hours fishing for men. As "bait," make posters of the Intelligence Test and IQ Test (from www.livingwaters.com/downloads/goodtest.pdf). Take advantage of the leisurely atmosphere to engage browsers in conversation, hand out tracts, and witness to those who stop to check out the test. In addition, have two or three people walking the aisles passing out tracts to others. Some of the easiest tracts to give away are the Giant Money and the Million Dollar Bill.

One church actually canceled their morning worship service to have the entire congregation pass out tracts at the local flea market. (In truth, this is the greatest act of worship—the Church leaving the four walls of the building and going into the world to seek and save the lost.) Then they decided to go a step further and rent a table at the flea market on Saturday, instead of meeting for their monthly men's breakfast. At least 1,000 people were given tracts that morning, and each man gave the "Good Person" test to at least 30–35 people. Many of those they spoke with were broken before God with their eyes welling up.

Joseph S., an elder from the church, said, "In twenty years of serving Christ, that was the highlight of my Christian walk. The men witnessing that morning unanimously agreed to rent a table once a month from now on. We had skeptics, Mormons, Jehovah's Witnesses, churchgoers, and pagans all walking past us on their way to hell. Perhaps, as Jude says, we were able to snatch some from the fire." Can you think of a better way to spend half a Saturday?

> **GREAT NEWS NETWORK**
>
> Check out **www.TheGreatNews.com** and locate others in your area who are using biblical evangelism. (Click on "Seed Sowers," then "Locate a Local Leader.") You will be greatly encouraged by the testimonies of Christians who use the Way of the Master techniques and you can even find others in your area to go witnessing with.

Words of Encouragement

The day after my first tracts arrived, I felt a strong urgency to go stand out front of the dance studio while my girls had their lesson, pass out tracts, and witness. But I thought, *Lord, this is Maine! It's cold outside!* I knew then my attitude had to change. I would rather freeze and stand outside than to let one single soul burn in hell.

Immediately after arriving I saw two young boys, dressed like gangsters, walking down the street toward me. I prayed for strength and boldness. I gulped and handed them an "Are You a Good Person" tract. *Whew! Now that wasn't so hard.* But then, before I knew what was happening, words came out of my mouth! I asked these boys if I could ask them a couple of questions. They said sure. For my very first time I was able to take two young men through the Good Person test. They were very receptive. They removed their bandanas, and the one who was smoking put out his cigarette. They even asked me questions about adultery. I shared with so much confidence I surprised myself! Neither wanted to go to hell and I was able to share with them what Jesus did so they wouldn't have to. It was incredible! Then I knew—I can do this!

Soon after they left, another young man came walking down. I handed him a tract and asked if I could ask him a few questions. Craig was so convicted his eyes were filled with tears. He said he was going into the Army, and had been praying the night before, because he knew he needed to be right with God. And here I was sharing with him! For the first time he *understood* the gospel. It made sense to him. Craig prayed right there to receive Christ!

I did all this in 35 minutes! And I am still in one piece! No one bit my head off and I didn't even realize how cold I was!

Thank you for teaching me to really love sinners. God is awesome and I am honored to live for Him and be a fisher of men!

—Donna H., Maine

For Deeper Study

1. Read Isaiah 47:10 and Psalm 50:21, and describe the atheist's view of God. How does this mindset violate the first two Commandments?

2. Some people claim it isn't possible to know if God exists, or to know Him personally if He does. What do the following Scriptures tell us?

   John 17:3; 1 John 5:20

   Acts 17:26,27; Jeremiah 29:13

3. Many intellectuals call themselves "agnostics," unaware that this is Greek for "ignorant." It's a shame to be ignorant when it's possible to acquire knowledge. How has God made His existence known?

   Psalm 19:1–4

   Acts 14:17

   Romans 1:20

4. Aside from the evidence of creation, what else has God given man to know He exists, according to the following verses?

   John 1:9; Luke 1:79

Romans 1:32; 2:15

5. Because all people have been given knowledge of God, what does Scripture say about the real reason for the agnostic's "ignorance"?

Jeremiah 9:6

Psalm 10:4

John 3:19,20

Romans 1:18–21

Ephesians 4:17–19

6. This type of ignorance is definitely not bliss. What does Acts 17:30 say to those who refuse to acknowledge God?

MEMORY VERSE

"He who has My commandments and keeps them, it is he who loves Me. And he who loves Me will be loved by My Father, and I will love him and manifest Myself to him."

JOHN 14:21

LESSON 8
Debunking Evolution

SHARE YOUR EXPERIENCES

Briefly discuss your witnessing encounters during the last week. Are you feeling more confident based on what you're learning in this course? Is evangelism becoming a way of life for you?

POINT TO PONDER

I recently found myself sitting in church during worship, staring at my thumb. I thought about how God made my thumb, and how blind we are to His incredible creative genius. Even those words fall infinitely short of how great God is. He made my thumb with the ability to bend one way, and remain firm and strong the other way. He made it with a unique thumbprint. With sensitivity. With skin that is soft and yet strong. He made the skin so that it would grow from a child's thumb into an adult's thumb. Inside are living bones, blood, and nerves. To be quite honest, I'm not really sure how the muscle structure and the sinews are put together, etc. I don't know where the thumbnail grows from and how it knows to grow on a curve. But it does.

As I thought about the amazing complexity of something as simple as my thumb, I thought about how I also have a thumb on my other hand, mirroring the one on my left hand. As I stared at my thumbs, I didn't bother to sing. It somehow seemed inadequate. I simply bowed my head in silence, and asked God to further open my shallow mind to the depth of who and what He is.

VIEW THE VIDEO Debunking Evolution (34 minutes)

Apply the Principles

1. What are some questions you can ask evolutionists to demonstrate the absurdity of the theory?

2. What does the phrase "missing link" mean?

3. If evolution were true, how many "transitional forms" would be needed, and how many have been found?

4. How would you respond to someone who claimed that similarities between men and apes proved a common ancestry?

5. What are some human abilities that primates lack? Why is this?

6. Finish this saying: "Man will believe anything, as long…"

7. What is the purpose for the existence of the Church?

8. Are you fulfilling that purpose? If so, how?

9. Explain the video's analogy of speaking to an unbelieving passenger on the plane. What's the best way to get him to put on the parachute?

QUALITY QUOTE

▶ *Leader's Note: Stand up and preach this as if you're speaking to your congregation.*

We are invited, brethren, most earnestly to go away from the old-fashioned belief of our forefathers because of the supposed discoveries of science. What is science? The method by which man tries to hide his ignorance. It should not be so, but so it is. [In the world's opinion,] You are not to be dogmatical in theology, my brethren, it is

wicked; but for scientific men it is the correct thing. You are never to assert anything very strongly; but scientists may boldly assert what they cannot prove, and may demand a faith far more credulous than any we possess. Forsooth, you and I are to take our Bibles and shape and mold our belief according to the ever-shifting teachings of so-called scientific men. What folly is this! Why, the march of science, falsely so called, through the world may be traced by exploded fallacies and abandoned theories.
—*Charles Spurgeon*

PREACHER'S PROGRESS

The characters: Christian and Eva Lution
Scene setting: Christian is at a college, speaking with an evolutionist named Eva.

Christian: "Did you get one of these? It's about the theory of evolution. It shows it to be false."

Eva Lution: "That's ridiculous! Evolution is a proven scientific fact."

Christian: "Scientific proof? What do you have?"

Eva Lution: "The appendix."

Christian: "How's that?"

Eva Lution: "The appendix! It has no purpose. It's an obvious 'leftover' from evolution."

Christian: "Is that scientific proof for the theory of evolution?"

Eva Lution: "Absolutely."

Christian: "Ear lobes don't have any real 'purpose,' and neither do male nipples, but that doesn't prove anything. Actually the appendix does have a purpose. It's part of the immune system."

Eva Lution: "I don't believe that. I'm an atheist and there's no way you can convince me that God exists. There is no scientific evidence for His existence. If I could see Him, then I would believe."

Christian: "Do you realize what you're saying? Look at the sun for thirty seconds and it will blind you for life; and yet the sun is only a small part of the creation of Almighty God. No one can see God and live. How long have you been an atheist?"

Eva Lution: "Three years. I used to be a Christian... until I saw the light. Christians are naïve simpletons who live on blind faith."

Christian: "You once knew the Lord?"

Eva Lution: "Yes... um... I mean... no... well, I thought I did."

Christian: "So you didn't know the Lord. You were only faking it? How long did that last?"

Eva Lution: "Um... about four years. I was in a youth group—took communion and all that."

Christian: "So, you proved to be a false convert. Like the Bible describes, in a time of tribulation, temptation, or persecution, you fell away. Do you consider yourself to be a good person?"

Eva Lution: "Of course."

Christian: "Have you ever told a lie?"

Again, don't spend too long in the area of the intellect. Go for the conscience, using the Law to bring the knowledge of sin.

CLOSE IN PRAYER

Words of Encouragement

Last year our church had a 10'×10' booth at the local county fair and gave Intelligence Tests (using the Survey Tract) and offered free candy. It was such a success that this year we doubled the booth size and spiced it up a bit. People attending the fair often have time to kill as they meander through exhibits and commercial buildings. We offered them a place to get off their tired feet, complete with 12 chairs for those taking and giving the tests (and sharing the gospel!). We blew up the big picture of Einstein [www.livingwaters.com/downloads/IQtestposter.zip], the two triangles illusion with an "extra square," and the "count the black dots" illusion [from the World's Best Optical Illusions tract].

The hottest tracts that people scooped up were "Everything Man Has Learned About Women," "101 of the World's Funniest One-Liners," "World's Best Optical Illusions," and "Hey, Kids." We made a timed PowerPoint show [www.livingwaters.com/downloads/fair_show.zip] of some funny one-liners and riddles to catch the eye of passersby. People would often laugh as they walked by and it helped start conversations and attract people to the IQ test.

This was absolutely the best "fishing hole" I've ever fished at. We had a total of 23 "test-givers" administer around 1,000 IQ Tests and passed out about 4,000 tracts in four days. The test questions served to build a good relationship with folks and when it came time to transition to the spiritual questions, they didn't run away—wonderful. Possibly the best part of the Survey Tract is the last question, "Do you avoid hell by living a good life?" If someone said yes, we would respond simply and quite naturally with, "Would you consider yourself to be a good person?" May county fairs and other witnessing spots across the world be filled with faithful fishermen.

— *Jared S., California*

Break Out of Your Comfort Zone

1. *Individual Activity:* Today, more than 5,000 people in the U.S. will die, and most of them will end up in hell. If you are horrified at that thought, it's because the love of God dwells in your heart, so let it cause you to do something to reach the lost. Witness to at least three people this week. Be intentional about it and create the opportunity. Don't wait for a "sign" or a feeling; just plan to go someplace where people congregate and do it.

   The need is great, so in addition to you being a faithful witness, you can teach other Christians how to share their faith biblically. This week, set a date and begin to show The Way of the Master Basic Training Course to a group of Christians. Promote it at your church and through your Bible study. It may be a houseful, or just a handful, or it may be only one other person. We know from experience that when some individuals get hold of this teaching they are transformed overnight into a fireball for the gospel. God may be waiting for you to call that person He wants to raise up. What are you waiting for? All you have to do is open your home, place a disk in a DVD player, and hit "play." Then sit back and have the joy of watching God work. You can do this. If your church doesn't have the Basic Training Course, you can go to www.WayoftheMaster.com to order it.

2. *Group Activity:* In addition to going to a weekly flea market or other site as your regular fishing hole, plan to set up a booth at any local fairs or festivals. Make large posters of the IQ Card tracts or other graphics to catch people's attention, and offer free food, water, small token gifts, or services to encourage people to stop and chat. To get ideas, read the "Words of Encouragement" for details on how one church did it—and had a blast.

   The key is to use your creativity to take advantage of every opportunity that comes your way to get the gospel into the hands of as many people as possible. Keep in mind Paul's words in 1 Corinthians 9:22: "I have become all things to all men, that I might by all means save some." Use all the means you can, as often as you can. Make witnessing not just a once-a-week (or less) event, but part of your daily life.

► *Leader's Note: To encourage others to learn to share their faith, ask your pastor if you can make a presentation to your church at the conclusion of the course. This is a good time to hand out the Certificate of Completion. As you do so, invite each of the participants to give a brief testimony of how the course has changed their life, and how their words may have helped to change the eternal lives of others. However, how people received your witness is not the point; your goal is not to get "decisions," but to faithfully plant seeds of the biblical gospel so people understand what they must do to be saved. That's always cause for rejoicing! Let the church in on your excitement at being used by God to speak to the lost about the Savior. Invite them to join you in following the way of the Master.*

For Deeper Study

True science and Scripture always agree, because they have the same Author. How does Scripture address the following scientific issues?

1. Science expresses the universe in five terms: time, space, matter, power, and motion. Read Genesis 1:1,2. How are each of these shown in the very first verses of Scripture, revealing that God controls of all aspects of the universe?

2. Scientists claim the universe began with a Big Bang. Yet they have no conclusive answer to where this matter and energy came from, or what caused it to go "bang." What explanation do Psalm 33:6,9 and Hebrews 11:3 give for how something can come from nothing?

3. Evolutionist Stephen Hawking, the best-known scientist since Albert Einstein, acknowledges "the universe and the laws of physics seem to

have been specifically designed for us. If any one of about 40 physical qualities had more than slightly different values, life as we know it could not exist: Either atoms would not be stable, or they wouldn't combine into molecules, or the stars wouldn't form the heavier elements, or the universe would collapse before life could develop, and so on." How can we explain these miraculous circumstances?

Nehemiah 9:6

Hebrews 1:2,3

4. The theory of evolution requires that at some point, non-living chemicals produced life. However, scientists have shown that "spontaneous generation" is impossible and that, according to the Law of Biogenesis, life can arise only from other life. Read Genesis 2:7 and Acts 17:24,25. How does God's Word solve their dilemma?

5. In what paleontologists call the "Cambrian Explosion," almost all major animal groups appeared suddenly, with no transitional forms preceding them. So instead of gradual change from simple to complex body types, fossils show that the major groups arose fully formed all at once. How does the fossil record confirm Genesis 1:20–25?

6. Microevolution, or natural selection, is variation within species (such as different dog varieties), which is provable. But Darwin's

84

theory is based on *macroevolution*, which claims that small changes within species can accumulate and create new species with new body types and features (such as a reptile growing wings). However, natural selection is always limited by the genetic code (it cannot "select" a feature that doesn't exist). Also, no transitional forms have ever been found. How does this scientific evidence match Scripture? See Genesis 1:11,12; 21; 24,25; 4:1; 1 Corinthians 15:39.

7. Researchers are finding that modern man shares genes with one male ancestor (dubbed "Y-chromosome Adam"), and that mankind spread out across the globe from one specific location. How does Scripture confirm this? See Genesis 1:27,28; 3:20; 1 Corinthians 15:45.

MEMORY VERSE

"For since the creation of the world His invisible attributes are clearly seen, being understood by the things that are made, even His eternal power and Godhead, so that they are without excuse."
ROMANS 1:20

Here are the answers to "Point to Ponder" in Lesson 7:

1. What is the name of the raised print that deaf people use?
   Deaf people don't use braille.

2. How many of each animal did Moses take into the ark?
   Moses didn't take any animals into the ark. It was Noah.

3. Spell the word "shop." What do you do when you come to a green light?
   You *go* at a *green* light.

4. Listen carefully. You are the driver of a train. There are thirty people on board. At the first stop, ten people get on. At the next stop, five people get off. Now for the question: What is the name of the train driver?
   You are the driver of the train.

5. It is noon. You look at the clock. The big hand is on three, and the little hand is on five. What time is it?
   It is noon.

Leader's Helps

This section will give you an overview of all the materials and preparation that are needed in this course. Facilitating the study doesn't require any special training, just a love for the Lord and for the lost. If you can simply follow the content given in the study guide, provide a few materials to participants, and plan some group activities, you are well qualified to lead this course with confidence. Have a positive attitude and expect God to do great things through your group!

PRINTABLE ITEMS

To help you inform others in your church about the Intermediate Training Course and encourage them to participate, we have included two promotional items on a CD for you to print in the desired quantity.

Provided are a 5.5" × 8.5" bulletin insert (printed two-up) and an 11" × 17" poster. These color files can also be printed in black and white.

Also provided is a printable Certificate of Completion, to give to those who successfully complete the course and put its principles into practice.

TRACTS

Ice Breakers are very valuable in sharing the gospel and are used heavily during this study. Unless participants are already witnessing using their own tracts, you will need to order tracts for their use. The course includes a Sample Pack for participants to choose from, so they can select their favorites to use throughout the course. Your church may want to purchase these for you as part of its outreach effort. Tracts can be ordered at www.WayoftheMaster.com.

To help you plan ahead, suggested activities that need preparation are listed below, along with any recommended tracts for each activity.

Before the Study Begins

Order one Study Guide for each participant. You may also want to order one pack of $1 Million Bills, to give a few to any participants who need them for the first week's homework.

Lesson 1

- Study Guide for each participant, and sufficient tracts to allow the group to complete the homework
- Sample Pack of tracts

Allow participants time to browse through the Sample Pack. Once they've selected their favorite tracts, place one order for the entire group to save on shipping costs.

Group Activity: Handing out tracts at a mall. Bring a small quantity of tracts.

Lesson 2

- Group Activity: PIE night (Pizza, Intercession, Evangelism). Plan an outing to a mall or other populated area, and bring plenty of tracts.

Suggested tracts include the Survey Tract.

Lesson 3

- Group Activity: Plan a fishing trip to a park, sports events, or mall, and bring plenty of tracts.

Lesson 4

- Group Activity: Door-to-door evangelizing. Plot out the target neighborhoods.

Suggested tracts include the Survey Tract and Are You a Good Person? You may also want to provide inexpensive New Testaments for homes that you visit.

Lesson 5

- Individual Activity: Place tracts in library books. Suggested tracts include Intelligence Test bookmarks, Good News & Bad News, and $1 Million Bills.

- Group Activity: Car wash. Get permission from a local business. Make signs (don't mention church name). Bring car wash materials.

Lesson 6

- Individual Activity: Make or purchase an "Are You a Good Person?" button. Suggested tracts include Are You a Good Person?

- Group Activity: Plan a fishing trip to a mall or other populated area, and bring plenty of tracts. Bring a video camera to film your witnessing encounters.

Lesson 7

- Paper and pen for each participant

- Group Activity: Flea market. Rent a table; provide eye-catching posters, a table covering, and plenty of tracts.

  Suggested tracts include $1 Million Bills and Giant Money.

Lesson 8

- Group Activity: Booth at a fair or festival. Rent a booth; provide eye-catching posters, a table covering, chairs, and plenty of tracts. You may want to offer free food, drinks, or small items.

  Suggested tracts include the Survey Tract, Optical Illusions, IQ Cards, Funniest One-Liners, and others. Money tracts ($1 Million Bills and Giant Money) are always easy to give out.

- Certificates of Completion

  If possible, make a presentation to the church about what you've learned in this course, and hand out the Certificates of Completion for all who attended the classes and put the teaching into practice. Otherwise, arrange a time of celebration to do this. Remember, there is no greater joy than leading others to find eternal life!

APPENDIX A
Quick Reference Card

To refresh your memory, the following text is from the Quick Reference Card contained in the Basic Training Course (available at www.WayoftheMaster.com). The acronyms WDJD and CRAFT will help you remember what to say as you make your way through a witnessing conversation. By following this outline, you will address the conscience as Jesus did, and present the gospel biblically. This is only a guide to enable you to hit the main points; feel free to use your own style and words.

WDJD

W *Would* you consider yourself to be a good person?

D *Do* you think you have kept the Ten Commandments?

J *Judgment*—If God were to judge you by the Ten Commandments, do you think you would be innocent or guilty?

D *Destiny*—Do you think you would go to heaven or hell?

CRAFT

C *Concern*—Does that concern you?

c *Cross*—Jesus suffered for our sins, died and rose from the dead.

R *Repentance*—Confess and forsake all sin.

A *And*

F *Faith*—More than belief, it's trust in Jesus for salvation.

T *Truth*—Point to the truth of the Bible and encourage them to get right with God today.

APPENDIX B
How to Witness Going Door to Door

When doing door-to-door evangelizing, a great way to get people's attention is to begin by offering to do small handyman chores for free. To do this, first put out a sign-up list at your church and make an announcement to the congregation, seeking people who are interested in using their handy skills to freely serve the community when occasionally called upon during a given weekend. This need will probably be rare and minimal.

Once you have five to ten people signed up, assemble a team to go door to door. Print some cards containing the church contact information, and then map out the homes in your community.

Be systematic about your approach and keep records of every address, jotting down the people's names and the type of response you received. This will come in handy for future visitations. Always be sure to go out in teams of two. No less and preferably, no more.

As you approach each door, begin by saying the following:

"Hi, how are you today? I'm so sorry to bother you at your home. I'll make this really quick. My name is _____ and this is my friend, _____. We're from _____, a local Christian church. We're not here to sell you anything or to get you to come to our church. We just wanted to let you know that we have a ministry set up to freely serve the community.

So, if you are ever doing any handyman work around your house, like painting, major gardening, putting up a fence, etc., we have a team of people from our church who are eager to come out and help you. There is no charge, and absolutely no donations will be accepted. And let me assure you that there are no strings attached. We just want to be a blessing to you. Here is card with our contact information. Please don't ever hesitate to call us. It would be our pleasure to serve you in any way we can.

We're also conducting a really quick questionnaire today. It's only three short questions and will take only two to three minutes. Would that be okay?"

The majority of the people, who at this point are blown away and blessed by your offer to freely serve them, are very open to take the questionnaire.

Here are the questions to the questionnaire:

1. "Do you believe in the existence of any type of God or higher power?"

2. "I'm sure you've heard of something called Judgment Day. This is said to be the day when everyone will be judged by God and receive either heaven or hell for all eternity. If there truly was a coming Day of Judgment, do you think it would be important for people to know what they would need to do in order to go to heaven and avoid hell?"

3. Depending on how they answered question 2, phrase the first part of this question in one of the following two ways:

    a. "Being that you believe this to be important, . . ."

    or

    b. "If you happened to be wrong and there was indeed a Judgment Day, . . . do you think you would know what a person would need to do in order to go to heaven and avoid hell, and if so what would you say that is?"

You may want to summarize these questions on a printed questionnaire. However, it's important for members of the witnessing team to memorize these questions if possible, rather than read them. They should glance down at the questionnaire for a second, just to remember the gist of the question, and then look the person in the eye when they ask it.

Place two columns under each question where the team member can mark a yes or no. It's not necessary to write down the person's answer about how someone can go to heaven and avoid hell.

If someone asks why the questionnaire is being conducted, an honest answer could be: "We are conducting this questionnaire in order to familiarize ourselves with the overall spiritual perspective of our community."

Once the questions have been asked, most people will begin to open up and share their opinions. It is very important that you listen attentively and closely at this point.

After they've finished sharing, transition by saying the following:

"Thank you so much. That concludes the questionnaire, but I had a couple of quick questions on a personal level: Would you consider yourself to be an open-minded person?"

Let them answer this. Then ask:

"And do you respect other people's beliefs?"

The overwhelming majority of people will answer yes to these two questions.

From that point you can springboard into the gospel by saying:

"I'm glad to hear that. Before we go let me quickly tell you what we believe about the coming Day of Judgment and what you can do to go to heaven and avoid hell, since this is the most important subject in the world."

Throughout the conversation you can refer back to the fact that they said they were open-minded and respectful of other people's beliefs, in order to reinforce what they are saying or to calm them down if they get upset. We've found this to be quite effective.

This approach has been used at approximately 1,000 homes and with countless people throughout the years on the street and in public places. By God's grace, it has been a fruitful approach.

While this is a good and proven format, remember it is important to be flexible to the leading of the Holy Spirit in the actual words that are used. This is simply meant to be a helpful guideline.

Additional Resources

For additional insight and tips on sharing your faith the way Jesus did, we invite you to sign up for our free monthly e-newsletter, which contains ministry updates, articles by Kirk Cameron and Ray Comfort, witnessing stories, notices of new Ice Breakers, special offers, etc. We want to be your witnessing resource center and a continual source of encouragement, inspiration, and blessing to you.

You can also gain further insights by listening to The Way of the Master Radio (www.WayoftheMasterRadio.com) and watching "The Way of the Master" television program (www.WayoftheMaster.com).

Don't miss these other helpful publications:

- *How to Live Forever without Being Religious*
- *Hell's Best Kept Secret*
- *The Way of the Master*
- *What Did Jesus Do?*
- *The Way of the Master for Kids*
- *How to Bring Your Children to Christ ... & Keep Them There*
- *Behind the Scenes: The Way of the Master*
- *Spurgeon Gold*
- *The World's Greatest Preachers*
- *How to Win Souls and Influence People*
- *God Doesn't Believe in Atheists*
- *Out of the Comfort Zone*

For a catalog of books, tracts, CDs, and DVDs by Ray Comfort and Kirk Cameron, visit www.livingwaters.com, call 877-496-8688, or write to: Living Waters Publications, P. O. Box 1172, Bellflower, CA 90706.

The Evidence Bible

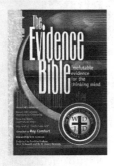

"*The Evidence Bible* is specially designed to reinforce the faith of our times by offering hard evidence and scientific proof for the thinking mind."
—Dr. D. James Kennedy

The Evidence Bible, based on more than two decades of research, has been commended by Josh McDowell, Franklin Graham, Dr. Woodrow Kroll, and many other Christian leaders.

- Learn how to show the absurdity of evolution.

- See from Scripture how to prove God's existence without the use of faith.

- Discover how to prove the authenticity of the Bible through prophecy.

- See how the Bible is full of eye-opening scientific and medical facts.

- Read fascinating quotes from Darwin, Einstein, Newton, and other well-known scientists.

- Learn how to share your faith with your family, neighbors, and coworkers, as well as Muslims, Mormons, Jehovah's Witnesses, etc.

- Glean evangelistic wisdom from Charles Spurgeon, John Wesley, George Whitefield, D. L. Moody, John MacArthur, and many others.

- Discover answers to 100 common objections to Christianity.

Find out how to answer questions such as: Where did Cain get his wife? Why is there suffering? Why are there "contradictions" in the Bible? . . . and much more!

School of Biblical Evangelism

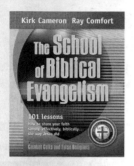

How would you like to be able to make an atheist backslide—in two minutes? Do you want to deepen your passion for the lost, for the cross, and for God? Then look no further.

Join more than 7,000 students from around the world in the School of Biblical Evangelism, to learn how to witness and defend the faith.

With 101 lessons on subjects ranging from basic Christian doctrines to knowing our enemy, from false conversions to proving the deity of Jesus, you will be well-equipped to answer questions as you witness to anyone. This study course will help you to prove the authenticity of the Bible, provide ample evidence for creation, refute the claims of evolution, understand the beliefs of those in cults and other religions, and know how to reach both friends and strangers with the gospel.

"A phenomenal course."
—Jim Culver

"Awesome . . . This course should be required in every theological seminary."
—Spencer S. Hanley

"As a graduate of every other evangelism course I can find, yours by far has been the best."
—Bill Lawson

"I have never seen anything as powerful as the teaching in the School of Biblical Evangelism."
—James W. Smith

Join online at **www.biblicalevangelism.com**
or call **800-437-1893**
to obtain the entire course in book form